D0363997

Mind-Boggling Code Breaker Puzzles
for Clued-up Kids

Editor: Lucy Dear
Contributors: Fran Pickering, Philip Carter, Nick Daws,
Peter Sorrenti, Ann Marangos, Claire Redhead
and Sarah Wells
Cover, page design and layout: Alan Shiner

Published by:
**Mad Moose for Lagoon Books 2003,
PO BOX 311, KT2 5QW, U.K.**

ISBN 1902813715

© 2003 Lagoon Books, London

mind-boggling

CODE BREAKER

puzzles

GREAT PUZZLES FOR CLUED-UP KIDS · GREAT PUZZLES FOR CLUED-UP KIDS

GREAT PUZZLES FOR CLUED-UP KIDS!

Other titles in the Mind-Boggling range include:

**MIND-BOGGLING
LATERAL THINKING PUZZLES
(For Clued-up Kids)**

**MIND-BOGGLING
TRICKY LOGIC PUZZLES
(For Clued-up Kids)**

**MIND-BOGGLING
BRAIN TEASER PUZZLES
(For Clued-up Kids)**

MIND BOGGLING
CODE BREAKER PUZZLES
FOR CLUED-UP KIDS

Psst! Do you like a challenge?
Fancy yourself as a bit of a detective?
Then we have a mission for you!

In this book you'll find a series of code-breaker puzzles.
Work out the code, and you'll be able to read the secret
messages they contain.

Each puzzle has a difficulty rating from 1 (fairly
straightforward) to 5 (would give Sherlock Holmes a
month of sleepless nights). The higher the difficulty rating,
the longer you can expect to take.

Your mission is to solve these puzzles as quickly as
possible. If you really get stuck, you can turn to the back
of the book for the answers -- but of course,
most of the time you'll only need to do this to confirm
that you're right.

So are you ready, special investigator?
Then take a deep breath, roll up your sleeves,
and turn the page. Good luck,
and remember – we need you to succeed!

Read All About It

The newspaper headline,
when unscrambled, reveals a secret coded message.
Can you unscramble it?

Cosmic Challenge

Difficulty Rating ☆☆

.sdnah dloh s'teL
.tenalp cimsoc ruo ot
emocleW

Archie the astronaut landed on an unknown planet.
A group of grinning aliens came towards him,
each holding out four hands and talking in a
high-pitched voice. That's odd! thought Archie.
I feel I ought to understand what they are saying!
Can you translate the alien language?

Missing Owner

Difficulty Rating ★★☆

Kate
Andrea
Theresa
Helen Edith
Rachel Irene Nancy
Elizabeth

On the school trip a suitcase was left on the bus.
Attached to it was a label.
How did the teacher know who owned the suitcase?

Cryptic Code

Difficulty Rating ★★★★★

Mike's Secret Society

EKQEA
ZIOL
QFR
NGXKT
OF

Mike and his mates have formed a secret society.
Mike's younger sister, Mandy, wants to join,
so Mike wrote a secret message for her.
"If you crack that, you can join", he said,
"but I warn you, it's hard!".
There is a clue to help you.

Clue: Use a computer or typewriter keyboard to help you.

Boy's Name

Difficulty Rating ☆☆☆☆☆

GNOMES (2)
LIKE (2)
HIDING (6)
UNDER (4)
LOGS (1)

Someone at Prank College put glue on the teacher's seat. Swotty Steven knows who did it and has sent a secret message to Mr Shouty the headmaster revealing the name of the naughty boy responsible. Using the numbers as a clue, can you help the headmaster to work out the name of the culprit?

Secret Ingredient

Difficulty Rating ★★★

Tomato Soup

Baked Goat's Cheese

ried Chicken

Chicken with Red Peppes

Apple Pie and Cstard

Cheesecake

Trfle

Mississippi Mud Pie

Cheese and Biscuis

Coffee and Mints

It's the Spies' annual convention and the chef has
created a special menu for the evening.
There is an extra item missing from the menu – study the
menu carefully and see if you can work out what it is.

Cartoon Caper

Difficulty Rating ☆☆

What is Jim's favorite cartoon?

Breakfast Bonanza

Difficulty Rating ☆

What did the spy have for breakfast?

Disco Dancers

Difficulty Rating ☆☆☆☆☆

The girls' high school has sent out invitations to
their annual ball. To make things even more exciting,
they have encoded the girls' names and put them in a
hat for each boy to pick one. Three friends – Steven,
Jake and Sam – have arrived together and picked their
papers. Steven picked '101145', Jake picked '111205'
and Sam picked '1911818'.
Who will be their dance partners?

14

Art Attack

Difficulty Rating ★★★★

Jim showed Laura his latest painting. "Kate gave it to me", he said, "although she knows I don't like abstract art. She said, however, it's a musical message." Laura studied the picture for a while then shouted, "Oh I get it. Just think of Britney Spears." Can you work out what the message is?

Quick Escape

Difficulty Rating ⭐⭐⭐

Fingers stole a fabulous jewel, worth a fortune.
Then he quietly left the country.
Which country did he escape to?

Wish You Were Here

Difficulty Rating ★★

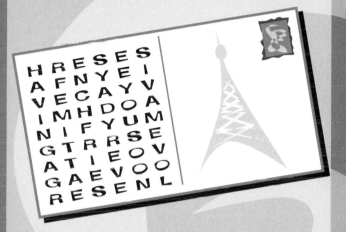

Daniel's friend sent him a postcard from France.
What does it mean?

Cartoon Watching

Difficulty Rating ☆☆

BCDOOOOSY

MSPDNEIRA

ACHIKPU

Three cartoon characters are appearing
at the school fair.
Can you work out who they are?

All the Fun of the Fair

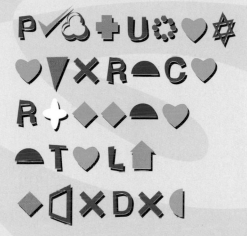

Jane's school is having a festival.
The highlight is a travel competition.
The names of five countries must be deciphered.
(See above - some letters have already been given
to help you.) Once you have deciphered the names,
the initials of those countries will spell out a city.
The winner's prize will be a trip to this city.
Can you work out what it is?

Football Position

Difficulty Rating ☆

25%

What position does Spencer play in football?

William Tell

Difficulty Rating ☆☆☆

William is on holiday and has sent the following letter
to his friend. Can you read what it says?

Meg's Secret Recipe

Difficulty Rating ☆☆☆☆☆

BERRIES

ORANGE

WINE

LEMONADE

BREAD

BANANA

GAGES

CLAM

CHOCOLATE

Aunty Meg has hidden the ingredients of her
secret recipe in this list. What are they?

Santa's Coming

Difficulty Rating ⭐⭐

Sandy wants something special for
Christmas – she's arranged the tree in such a way
that there's a hidden message for Santa.
Can you work out what she wants him to bring her?

Pairs

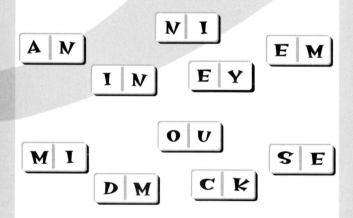

These dominos can be placed in a row to give
the names of a fictional couple that everyone knows.
Who are they?

Robot Wars

Difficulty Rating ✮✮✮

16 9 24

28 4 20

12 8 32

Robot number 4 has gone berserk.
Which number on its keypad will switch it off?

Clue: The number 4 has been shaded for a reason.

Open Sesame

Difficulty Rating ☆☆

When the new library was built, the staff room door was fitted with a computerized lock, seen here. Which button should the staff press to unlock the door?

Recipe Book

Difficulty Rating ✯✯✯

Rice Crispie Cakes

Melt half a large bar of chocolate in a
bowl over a pan of hot water.
Remove the bowl from the water.
Turn the heat off. Stir in handfuls
of rice crispies until the mix
is stiff and the crispies
are coated with chocolate.
Drop dollops of the crispie mix into
paper cake cases and leave to set.
Enjoy!

Famous people were asked to contribute their favorite
recipe to a cookery book. Whose recipe is this?

Forgetful Amy

Difficulty Rating ☆☆☆

CARD NO. 11325

Carol's Mum, Amy, could never remember her
ID card code. It was 11325.
"I know an easy way to remember it", said Carol,
"Just remember your name!"
How will this help her to remember her ID code?

How Old Is Ethel?

Difficulty Rating ★★☆☆

13	4	10	16	22
24	15	1	7	18
6	17	23	14	5
20	21	12	3	9
2	8	19	25	11

Grandma Ethel is a bit forgetful and cannot remember her age. Her husband Grandpa Jo gives her a grid to help her remember. Can you work out how old she is?

Batman and Robin

Difficulty Rating ☆☆☆

Batman decides to play a game with Robin.
He changes the lighting system of 8 apartment blocks
so that they reveal numbers. All Robin has to do is
add the numbers up to reveal Batman's age.
Can you work out Batman's age?

Garden Game

Difficulty Rating ★★★★

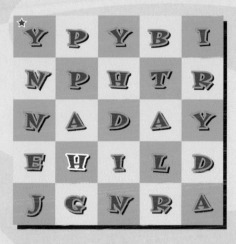

Mr and Mrs James mark their garden out into squares and give each square a letter. Their daughter, Jenny has to unravel the code by beginning at the red H and working from square to square horizontally and vertically, but not diagonally, finishing on the square marked with the star, to spell out a message.
Every square must be used once only.
What is the message?

Ancient Manuscript

Difficulty Rating ★★★★

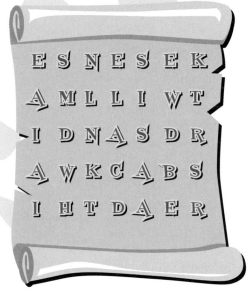

E S N E S E K

A M L L I W T

I D N A S D R

A W K C A B S

I H T D A E R

Professor Potts found an ancient manuscript.
It looked like it ought to make sense, but he couldn't
quite work it out. Can you?

Clue: the beginning isn't always the best place to start.

Cave Code

Difficulty Rating ☆

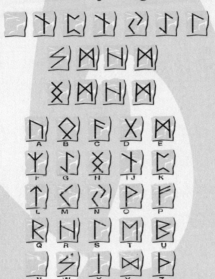

Eric the Explorer has found a wall carved with ancient runes. Could there be a message on it? Use the table of runes to work it out.

Computer Guess Work

Difficulty Rating ☆☆☆☆☆

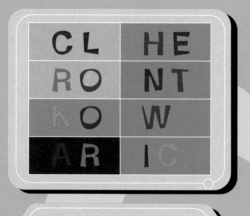

When Angela opens up her computer game,
the screen looks like this.
What does it mean?

Film Frenzy

Difficulty Rating ☆☆

Mary went to the cinema at the weekend.
Do you know what she went to see?

Clue: Say what you see.

Word Game

Difficulty Rating ★★★★

At Ron's birthday party each guest was given a card with two words on it. Each guest had to find one letter, which could replace the first letter of each word on their card to make two new words. For example:

Rate and Bone = G <Gate and Gone>

When you have found the letters, they should spell out a storybook creature.

Card Message

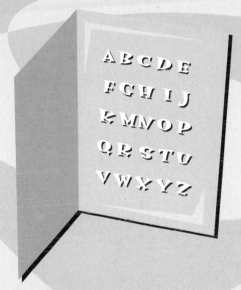

A B C D E
F G H I J
K M N O P
Q R S T U
V W X Y Z

On December 20th, Jane received this card.
What does it say?

Scientific Scrawl

Difficulty Rating ☆☆☆☆☆

Just before the intruders came to kidnap him,
the scientist scrawled a few numbers on a piece of paper
and slipped it under his old-fashioned telephone.
His friend found it later and knew who kidnapped him.
Can you work it out?

Free Ride

Difficulty Rating ★★★★★

Jane-Mary Moore, Susan O'Sullivan and Betty-Jean Anderson are standing outside the ice-cream parlor. Their friend Paul drives up to the girls, tooting his horn. Who is he offering a ride to?

Message Madness

Difficulty Rating ☆☆☆☆☆

69-87246-47
3352933-
23-84373-
28-6666

What is the important text message that Mary
has tapped into her mobile phone?

Odd Sentence

Difficulty Rating ✯✯

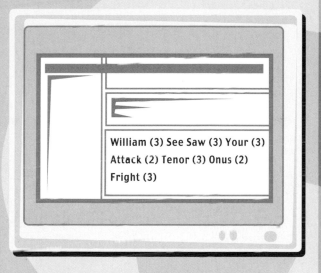

William (3) See Saw (3) Your (3)
Attack (2) Tenor (3) Onus (2)
Fright (3)

Milly sends Jim a cryptic email message.
Can you see what it is?

Number Cruncher

Difficulty Rating ☆☆☆☆☆

$$9.3.5.3.18.5.1.13 +$$
$$6.18.21.9.20 +$$
$$19.1.21.3.5 =$$

$$19.21.14.4.1.5$$

Alex the alphabet thief has substituted letters with numbers in this sum above.
Can you replace all the numbers with letters to reveal the name of his favorite dessert?

Party List

Difficulty Rating ☆☆☆☆

TOP SECRET

When	we	see	Marc
in	our	computer	area
next	week	we've to	knock
every	time	we're	here.

The twins are planning a surprise party for their mother's birthday. They need their Dad to buy two things on his way home from work, but don't want their mother to find out, so they slip him this note.

Secret Admirer

Difficulty Rating ☆☆☆☆

From Gill

UMBRELLA

URN

UTENSIL

UMPIRE

John finds a present in front of his hotel.
He looks at the label and smiles because he realizes
it's for him. How does he know this?

Alien Translation

Difficulty Rating ☆☆☆

The alien's translator has gone wrong.
Each word has one incorrect letter in it.
What is he saying?

Artifact Auction

Difficulty Rating ☆☆☆

This rare Indian necklace recently fetched a record
amount at auction. It is believed to have belonged to a
member of a tribe living by the side of a river.
By reading left to right can you tell which river it is?
A clue to help you is: Bottle = B

Christmas Gift

Difficulty Rating ★★

Jack has given his Mother this Christmas
wish list to pass to Santa Claus.
What is he asking for this year?

Soda Sum

Difficulty Rating ☆☆☆☆☆

How much does a soda cost?

Clue: There are 5 of them in the alphabet and each has a value.

Math Note

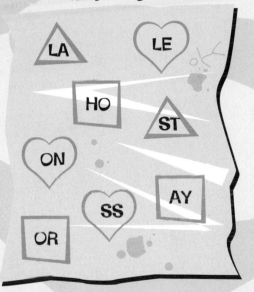

During math class Bart sent Sean a secret note.
What did it say?

Creature Code

Difficulty Rating ☆☆

What is Sue's favorite creature at the zoo?

Cartoon Caper

Difficulty Rating ☆☆☆

Peter's favorite cartoon is showing on the television.
Can you work out what it is?

Where's Lucy?

Difficulty Rating ☆☆☆☆☆

Lucy was a piano player, a traveling entertainer and a
part-time spy. One day a colleague friend from the Agency
called round to Lucy's house, only to find it deserted.
A scrap of music had been propped on a music stand.
The friend glanced at it, realised she knew where Lucy was
and went into town for lunch. Where was Lucy?

Secret Book

Difficulty Rating ♠ ♠

WOANDLERILACNED

Katy was not supposed to read in bed,
but she sneaked her favorite book into bed with her.
What is it?

Alien Jargon

Difficulty Rating ☆☆☆

Chris the Cosmonaut landed on an unknown planet.
As he stepped off his spacecraft, a smiling alien greeted
him with this odd message.
Can you work out what the alien is saying?

Secret Study

Searching the Professor's study for his Top Secret
formula, Jules found a row of boxes,
all labeled 'SECRET'.
Which one holds the secret formula?

Spelling Challenge

Difficulty Rating ☆☆☆☆☆

HE SNITRIT

E'M BIRAD.
SHULL WA GI UND
FREGHTAN SIMA
HOMUNS?
WA CIOLD HEDA
ONDAR BADS.
LIVA MOGWURT

Mugwart the monster wrote to his friend.
Mugwart wasn't a good speller, but his friend was
good at guessing. What did he write?
There is a clue to help you.

Clue: AEIOU

Sweet Success

A cake shop owner decided to sell pieces of a cake,
each decorated with a letter. The first customer
to combine six pieces of the cake into one round cake,
so that the six letters read correctly, will win a holiday.
Where is the holiday?

Puzzling Pin

Difficulty Rating ★★★

Nigel has problems remembering his 4-digit pass code when he does his shopping by computer, except when he brings the following up on his computer screen. What is his pass code?

Burglar's Secret

Difficulty Rating ★★☆

"Yesterday I decided to do some research on my new computer. It was a present from my Mum and Dad. I was looking for a gift for my best friend. She loves jewelry so I wanted to find her a gold necklace. I do not have much money so I was looking for something fairly cheap. After I had found a necklace I went for a ride on my horse Silverside. I rode over to my friend's house and we watched television. Looking at my watch I realized how late it was and rode home again. It had been a busy day!"

Two thieves are preparing a list of items they are hoping to steal when they break into the warehouse. They are encoding the 6 items they intend to steal so that the police cannot prove anything if the note is discovered. What are they planning to steal?

Lunch Note

Difficulty Rating ★★

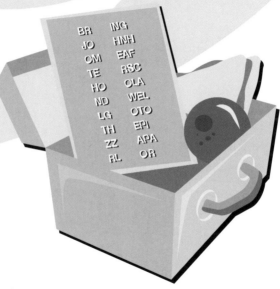

Kyle was keen on codes.
His Mum put this note in his lunch box.
What does she want Kyle to do?

Locker Room

Difficulty Rating ☆☆☆☆

Every time Tim visits the gym, he always chooses locker number 20913 for his towel. Why?

Ancient Message

WEARE   ENAND

CAVEM   WELIK

ETOPL   HDINO

AYWIT   SAURS

Professor McPuzzle was in his favorite place,
the museum archives, poring over ancient manuscripts.
One had recognizable letters, but what was written made
no sense – or did it?

Safe Turn

Difficulty Rating ☆☆☆

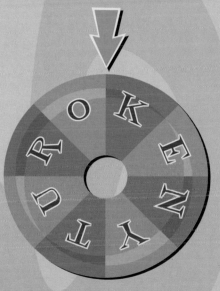

Turn the dial to the arrow in sequence, so that a
6-letter country is spelt out. This will open the safe.
To make things a little harder 2 of the letters
will not be used!

Mother Knows Best

Difficulty Rating ☆☆☆☆☆

To: Son@bedroom.com
From: Mother@kitchen.com

DIAL
EMU
VAN
ELASTIC
PATH

CAT
SEMI
DAM
PINE

A mother sends an email to her son
with this coded message.
Can you work out what it says?

Surprise Surprise!

Difficulty Rating ★★★☆

PARTY INVITATION!

Harry Andrew Larry Lenny Oswald William Eddie Edward Nigel

Kate Jenny Tonia

Nicholas Ian Gary Harry Thomas

Sarah Tracey Helen Betty

The children are planning a surprise party for
their parents and pass round a coded message to
reveal when the party will take place.
Can you decode their message?

Gang Rendezvous

Difficulty Rating ★★★★★

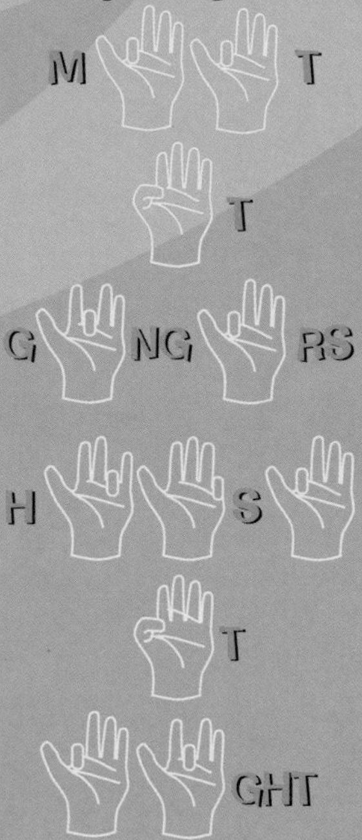

M   T

T

G   NG   RS

H   S

T

GHT

The Black Hand Gang had a secret code.
Can you crack it?

66

Safe Opening

Difficulty Rating ⋆⋆

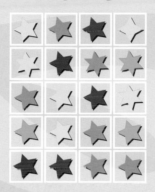

Called away on urgent business, Sarah phoned her husband, asking him to open her safe and send on a book she had forgotten. As usual she could not resist giving her instructions for opening the safe a cryptic twist as follows:

It is in a row or column, with a six-pointed star.
It is not beneath a red star.
It is one place from a blue star.
It is not above a green star.
It has a yellow star diagonally above it.

Can you help Sarah's husband work out which button to push to open the safe?

Love Letter

Difficulty Rating ☆☆☆☆☆

Jimmy wanted to send a message to his girlfriend while
he was on holiday, but didn't want anyone else to be able
to read the message on his postcard.
What was the message?

Missing Vowels

Difficulty Rating ★★

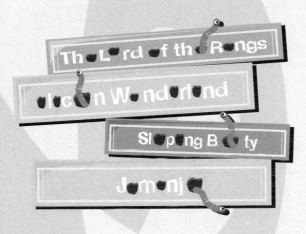

The Lord of the Rings

Alice in Wonderland

Sleeping Beauty

Jumanji

A bookworm has eaten all the vowels from
the book spines. Can you see what the titles are?

Treasure Chest

Difficulty Rating ☆

On a treasure hunt, if Patricia found a tap and
Garth found a rag, what did Pamela find?

TV Challenge

THE CIRCLE
RAISE YOUR
PRESS
TWICE AND
GREEN ARM

The TV game show Code Master is in full swing.
One of the clues looks like this. Can you work it out?

True Love

Difficulty Rating ☆

What does Patsy's Valentine card say?

Psst! Pass It On

Lxt's gx tx thx pxrk xftxr

schxxl xnd plxy txnnxs.

Shxll wx gxt xn xcx-crxxm

xn thx wxy?

Tom and Alice were passing notes to each
other in class. Their teacher,
Miss Jones, caught Tom as he passed his note
to Alice. Miss Jones read the note but she could not
understand it. Can you work out what it says?

Light Fingers

Difficulty Rating ☆☆☆☆☆

91	35	441	140	56
44	11	210	8	857
7	83	725	63	15	78
194	34	84	92	33
22	55	56	604	2

Which of the gang members stole the loot? Was it Jim, Fred, Sam or Tom? Brains knew, but was afraid to say, so he slipped this clue under the Boss's door giving him the first letter of the culprit's name.

Clue: 1 square has been shaded in – why?

Quick Escape

Difficulty Rating ✪✪

Fly Away

Seat No.

Aisle No.

Destination:

Cuba, America, Nepal, Africa, Denmark, Argentina

It looks as though the train robbers have succeeded,
but the police are after them and they don't want to
take any chances. They decide to flee the country and
Jon asks Pete to organize the tickets.
From this code can you work out where they are going?

Egyptian Secret

Difficulty Rating ☆☆☆

Daring Donald is searching a pyramid, in which a secret message is hidden. He must enter each room once only, in a continuous route, in order to spell out the 15-letter secret message. He may enter the outer corridor as many times as he wishes. What is the secret message?

Clue: Start at the black diamond.

76

Road Sign

Diffioulty Rating ✵✵

ELASPE

RIVED

YWLLOS

Overnight a strange new road sign went up
in the high street.
It didn't appear to make sense – but did it?

Round and Round

Difficulty Rating ☆☆

During the Olympic games,
all the gold medals were stolen.
Detective Schwarz found this hidden clue which shows
the thief's sport – can you help him to work out what
is the missing letter and reveal the thief's sport?

Time Warp

Difficulty Rating ★★★★★

9.N.3.15.13.9.N.7
T.R.1.V.5.L.L.5.R

In a secret underground center, scientists had built a time machine. Just as they were about to test it, it began to hum and this strange message flashed on the screen. Can you decipher it?

Weekly News

Difficulty Rating ☆☆☆☆☆

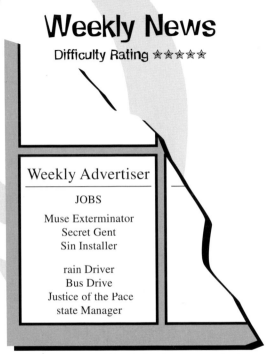

Weekly Advertiser

JOBS

Muse Exterminator
Secret Gent
Sin Installer

rain Driver
Bus Drive
Justice of the Pace
state Manager

Scarface placed the following unusual job
ads in a local paper. Crazy Bill studied these carefully
and smiled. He knew where the loot had been hidden.
Where is it waiting to be discovered?

Secret Treasure

Difficulty Rating ★★★

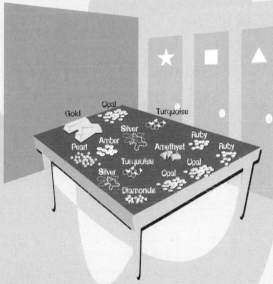

Will Hunt, the famous explorer, had found a cave with an amazing secret treasure. He excitedly phoned the news home, then disappeared. The rescue party found his hut empty except for a row of precious stones and gems on the table. Could they be a clue?

Safe and Sound

Difficulty Rating ☆☆

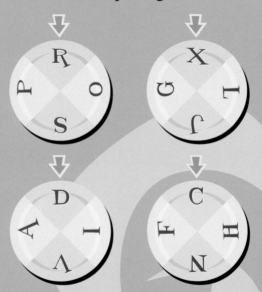

Turn the 4 dials, so that a 4-letter word is spelt
that will open the safe.
What is the 4-letter word?

Animal Magic

Difficulty Rating ☆☆

Jane loves going to the zoo,
but what's her favorite animal?

Solutions

Page 6 – Read All About It
ZOO CLOSED!
is an anagram of COOL DOZES!

Page 7 – Cosmic Challenge
The alien message was,
"Welcome to our cosmic planet.
Let's hold hands". The aliens
spoke recognizable words, but
they put the letters and the
words in reverse order.

Page 8 – Missing Owner
The first letter of each word is
used to spell the owner's name –
Katherine.

Page 9 – Cryptic Code
"Crack this and you're in."
Write out the letters of the
Alphabet, then underneath them
write the letters in the order they
appear on the computer
keyboard.

A B C D E F G H I J
Q W E R T Y U I O P

K L M N O P Q R S
A S D F G H J K L

T U V W X Y Z
Z X C V B N M

Page 10 – Boy's Name
Nigel.
The numbers indicate which letter
to select from each word.
Combining these letters spells the
boy's name.

Page 11 – Secret Ingredient
FRUIT - spelt out by the missing
letters.
Fried Chicken, Peppe**R**s C**U**stard
Tr**I**fle Bisui**T**s.

Page 12 – Cartoon Caper
Batman and Robin.
Bat + Man + (H)and + Robin.

Page 13 – Breakfast Bonanza
Scrambled eggs.

Page 14 – Disco Dancers
The numbers were a code for
each girl's name.
1=A, 2=B, 3=C etc.
Therefore Steven will dance with
Jane, Jake will dance with Kate
and Sam will dance with Sarah.

Page 15 – Art Attack
Each color and symbol
stands for a letter.

H = Holly
I = I
T = Table

M = Moose
E = Egg

B = B
A = Apple
B = B
Y = Yellow

O = Orange
N = N
E = Egg

M = Moose
O = Orange
R = R
E = Egg

T = Table
I = I
M = Moose
E = Egg

Hit Me Baby One More Time.

Page 16 – Quick Escape
Finland (F–in–Land).

Page 17 – Wish You Were here
Read down and up each
column in turn, from the left.
"Having a great time. French
fries every day! See you soon.
Love, Mavis."

Page 18 – Cartoon Watching
Scoobydoo Spiderman
Pikachu.

Page 19 – All the Fun of the Fair
Portugal, America, Russia,
Italy and Sweden.
The initials spell PARIS.

Page 20 – Football Position
Quarterback.

Page 21 – William Tell

Dear Kay,
I am at the seaside (the letter C is on its side!) Friday, we sailed to an island to fish. Today I am going to make a sandcastle and play football.
Your friend, Bill.

Page 22 – Meg's Secret Recipe

If you say aloud the color as well as the word then only some ingredients make sense. They are: blue berries, red wine, brown bread, greengages, white chocolate.

Page 23 – Santa's Coming

Barbie Doll.
The initials of each object spell out the word Barbie Doll. Bell, angel, reindeer, bell, iron, elephant, dove, orange, lantern, lime.

Page 24 – Pairs

| M | I | C | K | E | Y |

| A | N | D | M | I | N | N | I | E | M | O | U | S | E |

Mickey and Minnie Mouse.

Page 25 – Robot Wars

Press button 9.
It is the only number that is not divisible by 4.

Page 26 – Open Sesame

D.
Reading down each column the message says: press the orange button.

Page 27 – Recipe Book

Bart Simpson.
Rearrange the letters in red, bold type.

Page 28 – Forgetful Amy

The numbers relate to the position of the letters of A, M and Y in the alphabet.
A = 1
M = 13
Y = 25.

Page 29 – How Old Is Ethel?
All rows and columns add up to 65. So Ethel is 65.

Page 30 – Batman and Robin
30.
Look carefully at each apartment block, the pattern of on and off lights form the shapes of numbers.
$2 + 8 + 8 + 1 + 3 + 2 + 3 + 3 = 30.$

Page 31 – Garden Game

Happy Birthday Darling Jenny.

Page 32 – Ancient Manuscript

E S N E S E K
A M L L I W T
I D N A S D R
A W K C A B S
I H T D A E R

Read it backwards and the manuscript says:
"Read this backwards and it will make sense."

Page 33 – Cave Code
Vikings were here.

87

Page 34 – Computer Guess Work

"Click on the arrow."
Rearrange the letters until they make sense. Use the letter colors as a guide and group pairs of letters of the same color together.

Page 35 – Film Frenzy

Star Wars.
Star + W + Horse.

Page 36 – Word Game

GIANT.
Grip/Get
In/Ill
Aim/Alive
Nine/New
Time/Tin.

Page 37 – Card Message

Noel
(No 'L').

Page 38 – Scientific Scrawl

The KGB.
Each number represents a group of 3 letters on the dial. Try each letter until the message makes sense.

Page 39 – Free Ride

Paul is tooting in Morse Code. The message is Morse Code for SOS, which are Susan O'Sullivan's initials.

Page 40 – Message Madness

Mary's message reads:
"My train is delayed.
Be there at noon."
The mobile phone keys are arranged as follows:

2	3	4	5
abc	def	ghi	jkl

6	7	8	9
mno	pqrs	tuv	wxyz

Page 41 – Odd Sentence

Willam
See Saw
Your
Attack
Tenor
Onus
Fright

The numbers after the words relate to how many letters should be taken from the beginning of each word.
The message reads:
Will see you at 10 on Fri(day).

Page 42 – Number Cruncher

The numbers are a substitution code for letters of the alphabet, starting with A as 1 and ending with Z as 26.
The sum then reads:
ICE CREAM + FRUIT + SAUCE = SUNDAE.

Page 43 – Party List

Read down the first and last letters of each row.
Wine and Cake.

Page 44 – Secret Admirer

The four words all begin with U. 4 x U = For you.

Page 45 – Alien Translation

"Take me to your leader."
One letter in each word has been replaced with another.

Page 46 – Artifact Auction

AMAZON.

Apple = A
Mouth = M
Apple = A
Zebra = Z
Orange = O
Nose = N

Page 47 – Christmas Gift

Lots and lots of CDs.

Page 48 – Soda Sum

10c.
5c for every vowel in the name.

Page 49 – Math Note
Arrange the letters according to the shapes they're in, then rearrange them to reveal the message.
"Last Lesson. Hooray!"

Page 50 – Creature Code
Toucans.
Two Cans

Page 51 – Cartoon Caper
The Flintstones.

Page 52 – Where's Lucy?

Bagdad Café. The musical notes spelled out the place where she was.

Page 53 – Secret Book
Alice in Wonderland.

Page 54 – Alien Jargon
"Greetings Earthling!"
The alien put 'oblob' after every vowel.

Page 55 – Secret Study
C.
The word secret is on the top of the box - Top Secret!

Page 56 – Spelling Challenge
Use the following grid:

A E I O U
U A E I O

Hi Snotrot,
I'm bored. Shall we go and frighten some humans?
We could hide under beds.
Love, Mugwart.

Page 57 – Sweet Success
Brazil.

Page 58 – Puzzling Pin
4295.
The initials of each object
spell out the above number.
Frog, owl, umbrella, rabbit
Tree, window, ostrich
Nose, iceberg, nose, elephant
Frog, iceberg, van, elephant

Page 59 – Burglar's Secret
The items are hidden in the
text:

"Yesterday I decided to do
some research on my new
computer. It was a present
from my Mum and Dad. I was
looking for a gift for my best
friend. She loves jewelry so I
wanted to find her a gold
necklace. I do not have much
money so I was looking for
something fairly cheap.
After I had found a necklace I
went for a ride on my horse
Silverside. I rode over to my
friend's house and we
watched television. Looking
at my watch I realized how
late it was and rode home
again. It had been a busy
day".

Page 60 – Lunch Note
"Bring John home after
school and we'll go to the
Pizza Parlor."
Read the message across the
columns.

91

Page 61 – Locker Room
Using A = 1, B = 2 his name reads as '20-9-13'.

Page 62 – Ancient Message

The words are broken into blocks of 5 and then grouped in blocks of 2 rows.

Page 63 – Safe Turn
Turkey.

Page 64 – Mother Knows Best

The last letters of each word spell out the word LUNCH TIME.

Page 65 – Surprise Surprise!
Halloween Night.
Take the initials of the boys' names only.

Page 66 – Gang Rendezvous
MEET AT GINGER'S HOUSE AT EIGHT.
The gang replaced the vowels with a hand signal for each one.

Page 67 – Safe Opening

The shaded pink 5 pointed star (third column, fourth row down).

Page 68 – Love Letter
MISSING U.
(U is missing from the alphabet)

Page 69 – Missing Vowels
1. The Lord of the Rings
2. Alice in Wonderland
3. Sleeping Beauty
4. Jumanji

Page 70 – Treasure Chest
A map.
Reverse the first three letters of each name to spell out the three things. Patricia (tap), Garth (rag) and Pamela (map).

Page 71 – TV Challenge
"Press the green circle twice and raise your arm."
Join the words in the order of the colors of the rainbow. Red, Orange, Green, Blue, Indigo, Violet.

Page 72 – True Love
I love you (Ewe).

Page 73 – Psst! Pass it on
Tom had replaced all the vowels with an X.
The message reads:

Let's go to the park after school and play tennis.

Shall we get an ice-cream on the way?

Page 74 – Light Fingers
Shade in all the squares that contain a number that can be divided by 7. The letter T appears, so Tom must be the thief.

Page 75 – Quick Escape
Canada.
The initials of each country spell out the word Canada.

Page 76 – Egyptian Secret

Gold and Gems here.

Page 77 – Road Sign
Please drive slowly.
The letters of each word have been jumbled up.

Page 78 – Round and Round
E.
Starting from the second R, the letters spell out the word RUNNER.

Page 79 – Time Warp

INCOMING TRAVELLER.
Every other letter of the
Alphabet has been numbered

A	1	N	N
B	B	O	15
C	3	P	P
D	D	Q	17
E	5	R	R
F	F	S	19
G	7	T	T
H	H	U	21
I	9	V	V
J	J	W	23
K	11	X	X
L	L	Y	25
M	13	Z	Z

Page 80 – Weekly News

The loot is hidden under the
Oak tree. Each line is missing
a letter. The letters spell out
"Oak tree."

Weekly Advertiser

JOBS
MOuse Exterminator
Secret Agent
SinK Installer

Train Driver
Bus DriveR
Judge of the PEace
Estate Manager

Page 81 – Secret Treasure

The initial letters of the names
of the gems spell out:
Go Past Star Door.

Page 82 – Safe and Sound

PLAN.

Page 83 – Animal Magic

The Elephants.
The letters when rearranged
spell Elephant.

LAGOON
BOOKS